Tony Gaddis

Starting Out
With Programming
Logic & Design
Lab Manual

Custom Third Edition

Taken from:
Starting Out With Programming Logic & Design Lab Manual, Third Edition
by Tony Gaddis

ISBN 10: 1-256-41260-0
ISBN 13: 978-1-256-41260-1

Contents

Lab 1:   Introduction to Computers and Programming 1
 Lab 1.1 GUI vs. Console Programming...1
 Lab 1.2 Using Visual Basic IDE 3
 Lab 1.3 Design Tools 6

Lab 2:   Input, Processing, and Output 9
 Lab 2.1 Pseudocode 9
 Lab 2.2 Flowchart 11
 Lab 2.3 Visual Basic 13

Lab 3:   Input, Processing, and Output 15
 Lab 3.1 Pseudocode 15
 Lab 3.2 Flowcharts...17
 Lab 3.3 Visual Basic 18
 Lab 3.4 Programming Challenge—Network Systems Administration....................20

Lab 4:   Modules 21
 Lab 4.1 Pseudocode and Modules 21
 Lab 4.2 Flowcharts and Modules 24
 Lab 4.3 Visual Basic and Modules..27
 Lab 4.4 Challenge: Ping and Website Launches 30

Lab 5:   Decisions and Boolean Logic I 33
 Lab 5.1 Evaluating Conditions with Relational Operators 33
 Lab 5.2 Evaluating Conditions with Logical Operators 34
 Lab 5.3 Pseudocode 35
 Lab 5.4 Flowcharts...38
 Lab 5.5 Visual Basic 40

Lab 6:   Decisions and Boolean Logic II..43
 Lab 6.1 Pseudocode 43
 Lab 6.2 Flowcharts...46
 Lab 6.3 Visual Basic Programming Challenge 48

Lab 7:   Repetition Structures I 51
 Lab 7.1 Condition Controlled with While and Do-While Loops: Pseudocode 51
 Lab 7.2 Condition Controlled with While and Do-While Loops: Flowcharts..........53
 Lab 7.3 Count Controlled with While and Do-While Loops: Pseudocode..............55
 Lab 7.4 Count Controlled with While and Do-While Loops: Flowcharts 57
 Lab 7.5 While and Do-While Loops: Visual Basic Challenge I 58
 Lab 7.6 While and Do-While Loops: Visual Basic Challenge II............................60

Lab 8:   Repetition Structures II..**61**
    Lab 8.1 For Loop and Accumulation with Pseudocode...............................61
    Lab 8.2 For Loop and Accumulation with Flowcharts 65
    Lab 8.3 Accumulation and Loops: Visual Basic Challenge.......................67

Lab 9:   Functions and Input Validation **69**
    Lab 9.1 Functions in Pseudocode and Visual Basic...................................69
    Lab 9.2 Programming Challenge: Functions and Visual Basic...................73
    Lab 9.3 Input Validation..75
    Lab 9.4 Programming Challege: Cell Phone Minute Calculator 78

Lab 10:   File Access **81**
    Lab 10.1 File Access and Visual Basic 81
    Lab 10.2 File Access and Nested Loops 84

Lab 1: Introduction to Computers and Programming
This lab accompanies **Chapter 1** of *Starting Out with Programming Logic & Design.*

Lab 1.1 – GUI vs. Console Programming

Critical Review

When starting a project, a programmer can decide whether to create a GUI or a console (command line) project.

Graphical User Interface (GUI) programming:
GUI programming is a complex process that uses the computer's graphic features such as mouse pointers, icons, and menus to allow the user a point and click environment.

Console programming:
Console programming is easy, fast, and useful. It is most commonly used when an advanced user interface such as a GUI is not necessary. This course will create console applications in order to focus on the programming logic behind coding.

The .exe:
.exe or executable files are used to run or install programs. A programmer typically shares or sells an .exe, and not the code that was used to create the executable. The user of programs typically does not know what language was used to create an executable.

Demo Video: View *lab1-1.wmv* **in the Lab 1 folder on the accompanying Lab Demo Media and Startup Files CD.**

This lab requires you to execute both types of programs to understand the differences.

Step 1: Double click on the file named *consoleapp.exe* in the Lab 1 folder on the accompanying Lab Demo Media and Startup Files CD, and run the program.

Step 2: Double click on the file named *guiapp.exe* in the same folder and run the program.

Step 3: Answer the following questions:
  1. What similarities do you see between the two programs?

  2. What differences do you see between the two programs?

3.   What input devices are used in the GUI and console programs?

4.   What output devices are used in the GUI and console programs?

P@$$wOrd

Lab 1.2 – Using Visual Basic IDE

Critical Review

Visual Basic (commonly known as VB) is a Microsoft programming language and software development environment that allows programmers to create Windows-based applications quickly. It also allows you to create Console applications, as you will create throughout this course.

Demo Video: View *lab1-2.wmv* in the Lab 1 folder on the accompanying Lab Demo Media and Startup Files CD

This lab requires you to use the IDE (Integrated Development Environment) to create a project workspace using Visual Basic 2005.

Step 1: Launch Visual Basic 2005. Click on File, then New Project. In the template window, select Console Application. In the Name box, enter a name for your program. Click OK to create your workspace.

Step 2: Save your program. Click on File, then Save All. You can choose your workspace location. Click Save.

Step 3: All programming code will go inside Main( ). This is automatically inserted into your workspace so you are ready to code.   Copy and paste the code that shows up in your window into a Word document.

Step 4: Click on File, and Exit your program. Be sure to click Save All if it is not saved.

Step 5: Launch Visual Basic again. When you open a previously created workspace, click File, then Open Project. In order to open all the files associated with your workspace, you must open the .sln file. Find that, and click Open.

If the code window does not show, click View, then Solution Explorer. Double Click on Module1.vb. That is the name of the code file, although you need the entire workspace open in order to run your application.

Step 6: Inside Main( ), type the following exactly:

```
Console.WriteLine("This is my first program")

'this causes a pause so you can see your program
Console.Write("Press enter to continue...")
Console.ReadLine()
```

Step 7: Click on Build, then Build your program. This creates your .exe. Click on Debug, then Start Debugging. This will run your program.

Step 8: Under Edit, click Select All, then Copy. Paste your programming code into the document created for Step 3.

Lab 1.3 – Design Tools

> **Critical Review**
>
> Before you begin coding, there are two tools that will help you logically design a program. They are Pseudocode and Flowcharts.
>
> Pseudocode is an informal use of language that has no syntax rules. It is simply words that describe step by step what a program does.
>
> A flowchart is a diagram that graphically depicts the steps that take place in a program.
>
> Both will be further explained later and used throughout this course.

Demo Video: View *lab1-3.wmv* in the Lab 1 folder on the accompanying Lab Demo Media and Startup Files CD

This lab requires you to examine the flowcharting tools you might use with this course. While designing flowcharts can be done with paper and pencil, one mistake often requires a lot of erasing. Therefore, a flowcharting application such as Raptor or Visio should be used. This lab will give you a brief overview of Raptor and Visio.

Step 1: Start Raptor; notice the Raptor screen. This window is your primary tool for creating a flowchart. Prior to adding symbols, save your document by clicking on File and then Save. Select your location and save the file. The *.rap* file extension will be added automatically.

Step 2: Notice the MasterConsole screen. This window is used to show your program output once your flowchart is completed. The Clear button will clear the console to view a fresh run of your program.

Step 3: Click File and Exit to close Raptor.

Step 4: Double click on the file named *lab 1-3raptor.rap* in the Lab 1 folder on the accompanying Lab Demo Media and Startup Files CD to see the raptor flowchart. You may have to click on the file and save it to your work area in order for it to run properly.

Step 5: Click on Run and then Execute to Completion on the Raptor menu. Follow the flow of the program to see the program process. The MasterConsole window should show output.

Step 6: Copy and paste what you see in the MasterConsole window into a separate Word file. Exit Raptor.

An alternative flowcharting tool is Microsoft Visio.
Step 7: Launch Microsoft Visio. Under Template Categories, select Flowcharts. Under Featured Templates, select Basic Flowchart. Save your file to your workspace area.

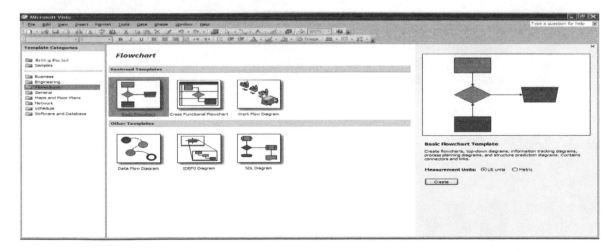

Step 8: The Shapes windows list flowcharting shapes. You can click and drag these to the work grid. Double click on the file named *lab 1-3visio.vsd* in the Lab 1 folder of the

accompanying Lab Demo Media and Startup Files CD to see what a Visio flowchart looks like. Visio files have a .vsd extension.

Lab 2: Input, Processing, and Output

This lab accompanies **Chapter 2 (pp. 29-55)** of *Starting Out with Programming Logic & Design*.

Lab 2.1 – Pseudocode

Critical Review

Pseudocode is an informal language that has no syntax rules and is not meant to be compiled or executed.

The flow the program takes is sequential. For example, before you ask for input, you should display what information you want from the user.

Follow the rules for naming variables: (1) must be one word, no spaces, (2) usually no punctuation characters, only letters and numbers, and (3) name cannot start with a number.

"Display" is the keyword used to print something to the screen. Any information needed to be displayed to the user should be put inside quotation marks such as *Display "This is how you print something to the screen"*. When using display to print both a string and the value of a variable, a comma is used, such as *Display "Here is the average", average*.

"Input" is the keyword used to get the user to enter data. The data value entered by the user will be placed in the variable that follows the keyword input such as *Input variableName*.

"Set" is the keyword used before a calculation. Standard math operators are used, such as + - * / MOD ^. Operators can be combined in one calculation, but it is wise to group expressions together using parentheses. Remember the order of operations. Some examples are *Set sale = price – discount* and *Set average = (test1 + test2 + test3) / 3*.

Demo Video: View *lab2-1.wmv* in the Lab 2 folder on the accompanying Lab Demo Media and Startup Files CD.

This lab requires you to focus on variable assignment and calculations. Read the following program prior to completing the lab.

```
Write a program that will calculate the cost of installing
fiber optic cable at a cost of .87 per ft for a company.
Your program should display the company name and the total
cost.
```

Step 1: Examine the following algorithm as a base for how the program should flow. (Reference: Designing a Program, page 31).

```
1. Display a welcome message for your program.
2. Get the company name.
3. Get the number of feet of fiber optic to be installed.
4. Multiply the total cost as the number of feet times .87.
5. Display the calculated information and company name.
```

Step 2: Think of good variable names for the following pieces of data that will need to be stored with in this program.

Purpose of Variable	Variable Name
Stores the cost of fiber	fiberCost
Stores the company name	
Stores the number of feet to be installed	
Stores the calculated cost of installed fiber	

Step 3: Complete the following pseudocode based on the algorithm and the variables you declared above.

```
Display "Welcome to the Fiber Optic Calculator Program"
Set fiberCost = ?
Display "What is the company name?"
Input ?
Display "How many feet of fiber will be installed?"
Input ?
Set ?
Display "For the company", ? ,"the total cost will be $",?
```

Lab 2.2 – Flowchart

Critical Review

A flowchart is a diagram that graphically depicts the steps that take place in a program. Symbols are used to depict the various steps that need to happen within a program. Flow lines are used between the symbols to indicate the flow of the program.

Ovals are used as terminal symbols, which indicate a start and stop to a program.

Parallelograms, the data symbol, are used for input and display statements.

Rectangles, the process symbol, are used for calculations and variable declarations.

On page connectors are used to link a flowchart that continues on the same page. The connecting system starts with the letter A, whereas A would appear in the two connectors that show the flow.

The statements inside the data and the process symbols can be written similarly to the statements used in pseudocode.

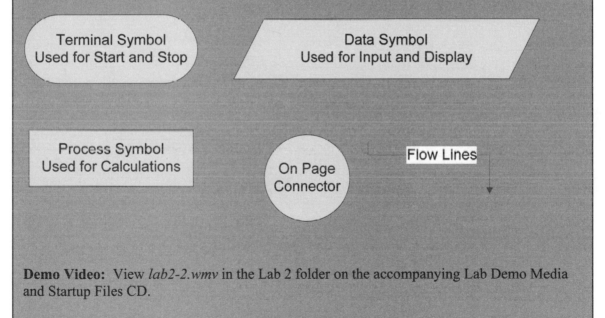

Demo Video: View *lab2-2.wmv* in the Lab 2 folder on the accompanying Lab Demo Media and Startup Files CD.

This lab requires you to think about the steps that take place in a program by designing a flowchart. While designing flowcharts can be done with paper and pencil, one mistake often requires a lot of erasing. Therefore, a flowcharting application such as Raptor or Visio should be used. This lab will give you a brief overview of Raptor. Read the following program prior to completing the lab.

```
Write a program that will calculate the cost of installing
fiber optic cable at a cost of .87 per ft for a company.
Your program should display the company name and the total
cost.
```

Step 1: Launch Raptor or Visio and convert your pseudocode from Lab 2-1 into a flowchart. Depending on what application you are using, select either *lab2-2raptor.rap* or *lab2-2visio.vsd* from the Lab 2 folder on the accompanying Lab Demo Media and Startup Files CD to get started. **Once you double click on them to open, do a Save As to save it to your workspace.** Watch the demo video 2-2 for instructions on how to input, calculate, and output using both applications.

Step 2: The final step is to insert your finished flowchart into a Word document. Inside Raptor, select File and then Print to Clipboard from the menu. If you are using Visio, select Edit, then Select All, then Edit and Copy. In your Word document, select Edit and Paste.

Lab 2.3 – Visual Basic

Critical Review

Console.WriteLine("....") or Console.Write("...") is similar to the Display keyword in pseudocode. Console.WriteLine includes a return at the end of the display, and Console.Write leaves the cursor on the current line. We use these functions to write information to the screen. You can display string literals or string literals with variables such as:

```
Console.WriteLine("The number is " & aNumber)
Console.WriteLine("This is a sentence")
```

The & is used to connect a string literal with a variable.

Console.ReadLine( ) or Console.Read is used to take in input into a variable. Since variables must be declared before input can be used, this will be further explored in Lab 3.

Dim (meaning Dimensions) is the keyword to declare variables. We will set some values of variables in the lab 2-3, but will reserve explanation of data types such as Double, Integer, and String for Lab 3. To set values of variables in Visual Basic, use the following syntax.

```
Dim dollars As Double = 2.75
Dim myAge As Integer = 35
```

Demo Video: View *lab2-3.wmv* in the Lab 2 folder on the accompanying Lab Demo Media and Startup Files CD

This lab will focus on how to assign variables and process calculations in Visual Basic.

Step 1: Create a new Visual Basic Console Application and save it to your workspace location.

Step 2: The first part of this program will convert the pseudocode from page 44 to Visual Basic. Under `Sub Main()` add the following line of code.

```
Console.WriteLine("This part of the program will code Program 2-6
from page 44")
```

You can also use Console.Write( ) if you want the cursor to stay on the same line as your output.

Step 3: Following the steps on page 44, next declare dollars such as:

```
Dim dollars As Double = 2.75
```

Step 4: Using Console.WriteLine( ) code step 2 from Program 2-6 such as:

```
Console.WriteLine("I have " & dollars & " in my account.")
```

Notice the & are used in Visual Basic and , are used in pseudocode.

Step 5: Reset dollars to 99.95 by adding the following:

```
dollars = 99.95
```

Step 6: Convert step 4 from page 44 to display what is now in the account. You can follow the Visual Basic syntax from Step 4 of this lab.

Step 7: At the very bottom before End Sub add the following lines so that your program will Pause and you can see your output.

```
Console.WriteLine("Press any key to continue")
Console.ReadLine()
```

Step 8: Save and run your program so that it works without errors. Copy and paste your Visual Basic code into a Word document.

Real   45.5

Int   45

Lab 3: Input, Processing, and Output
This lab accompanies **Chapter 2 (pp. 56-68)** of *Starting Out with Programming Logic & Design.*

Lab 3.1 – Pseudocode

> **Critical Review**
>
> //Comments are done by putting two forward slashes before the lines you want to //document. Comments are used to explain code.
>
> Variables are named storage locations.
>
> "Declare" is the keyword used before naming a variable.
>
> Data types are: Real for decimal numbers, Integer for whole numbers, and String for a series of characters.
>
> **Demo Video: View *lab3-1.wmv* in the Lab 3 folder on the accompanying Lab Demo Media and Startup Files CD.**

This lab requires you to think about the steps that take place in a program by writing pseudocode. Read the following program prior to completing the lab.

```
Write a program that will take in basic information from a
student, including their name and how many credits they
have taken in Network Systems Administration program.  The
program will then calculate how many credits are needed to
graduate.  Display should include the student name and the
number of credits left to graduate.  This should be based
off a 90 credit program, where some courses are half
credits.
```

Step 1: This program is most easily solved using just a few variables. Identify potential problems with the following variables declared in the pseudocode. Assume that the college has the ability to offer half credits. (Reference: Variable Names, page 39-40).

Variable Name	Problem (Yes or No)	If Yes, what's wrong?
Declare Real creditsTaken		
Declare Int creditsLeft		
Declare Real studentName		
Constant Real credits Needed = 90		

Step 2: What is wrong with the following calculation? (Reference: Variable Assignment and Calculations, page 43).

```
Set creditsLeft = creditsTaken - creditsNeeded
```

_____

_____

Step 3: Write the exact output you would expect from the following line of code if the user of the program enters "Nolan Owens". (Reference: Displaying Items, page 40 – 41).

```
Display "The student's name is ", studentName
```

_____

Step 4: Write the exact output you would expect from the following line of code if the user of the program enters a name of Nolan Owens and they have taken 20 credits so far. (Reference: Displaying Items, page 40 – 41).

```
Display "The Network Systems Administration degree is
awarded after 90 credits and ", studentName, " has ",
creditsLeft, " left to take before graduation."
```

_____

Step 5: Complete the following pseudocode to solve the programming problem.

```
1. //Provide documentation on line 2 of what this program does
2. //

3. //Declare variables on lines 4, 5, 6, and 7
4.
5.
6.
7.

8. //Ask for user input of studentName and creditsTaken on
   line 9 - 12.
9.
10.
11.
12.

13. //Calculate remaining credits on line 14
14.

15. //Display student name and credits left on line 16 and 17
16.
17.
```

> Critical Review
>
> A flowchart is a diagram that graphically depicts the steps that take place in a program. Symbols are used to depict the various steps that need to happen within a program. Flow lines are used between the symbols to indicate the flow of the program.
>
> **Demo Video: View *lab3-2.wmv* in the Lab 3 folder on the accompanying Lab Demo Media and Startup Files CD.**

Lab 3.2 – Flowcharts

This lab requires you to think about the steps that take place in a program by designing a flowchart using either Raptor or Visio. Read the following program prior to completing the lab.

```
Write a program that will take in basic information from a
student, including their name and how many credits they
have taken in Network Systems Administration program.  The
program will then calculate how many credits are needed to
graduate.  Display should include the student name and the
number of credits left to graduate.  This should be based
off a 90 credit program, where some courses are half
credits.
```

Step 1: Launch Raptor or Visio and convert your pseudocode from Lab 2-1 into a flowchart. Depending on which application you are using, select either *lab3-2raptor.rap* or *lab3-2visio.vsd* from the Lab 3 folder on the accompanying Lab Demo Media and Startup Files CD to get started**. Once you double click on them to open, do a Save As to save it to your workspace.** Watch the demo video 3-2 for instructions on how to input, calculate, and output using both applications.

Step 2: The final step is to insert your finished flowchart into a Word document. Inside Raptor, select File and the Print to Clipboard from the menu. If you are using Visio, select Edit, then Select All, then Edit and Copy. In the Word document, select Edit and Paste.

Lab 3.3 – Visual Basic

Critical Review

Documentation/comments in Visual Basic are preceded by a single quote such as 'This line will be commented out and usually results in green text

The most popular data types in Visual Basic are String (for a letter or word), Double (for a real), and Integer (for a whole number). It is also common practice to initialize variables to a value of 0 before they are used such as:

```
Const fiberCost As Double = 0.87 'this can be a constant
Dim companyName As String = "NO VALUE"
Dim age As Integer = 0
```

Const is the keyword to declare a variable as a constant.

Declaring variables must be done before they can be used, so often they are at the top of your code.

Console.ReadLine() is used to take in the value of a String or Numberic variable.

```
Console.Write("Enter company name ")
companyName = Console.ReadLine()

Console.Write("How many feet are to be installed ")
numFeet = Console.ReadLine()
```

Demo Video: View *lab3-3.wmv* in the Lab 3 folder on the accompanying Lab Demo Media and Startup Files CD.

This lab requires you to convert the following problem into an actual program using Visual Basic.

```
Write a program that will calculate the cost of installing
fiber optic cable at a cost of .87 per ft for a company.
Your program should display the company name and the total
cost.
```

Step 1: Launch Visual Basic and create a new Console Application. Save it to the appropriate location.

Step 2: All code will go between of Sub Main( ) and End Sub. Start by declaring and initializing your variables such as:

```
'local variables used in this program
```

```
Const fiberCost As Double = 0.87
Dim companyName As String = "NO VALUE"
Dim numFeet As Double = 0
Dim totalCost As Double = 0
```

Step 3: Using Console.Write("…"), ask the user to enter the company name. Then, using Console.ReadLine(), write a line of code that will allow the user to enter the name of the company. This might look like:

```
Console.Write("Enter company name ")
companyName = Console.ReadLine()
```

Step 4: Next, using Console.Write("…"), ask the user enter the number of feet of fiber to be installed. Then, using Console.ReadLine( ), write a line of code that will allow the user to enter numFeet.

Step 5: Next, process your calculation such as:

```
totalCost = numFeet * fiberCost
```

Step 6: Using Console.WriteLine("…"), display the name of the company and the total cost of the installation to the screen. Remember, use the & within the quotes if you want to place the value of a variable within a sentence.

Step 7: Finally, add your makeshift Pause so that the screen will pause before it ends. This should be coded such as:

```
'this causes a pause so you can see your program
Console.Write("Press enter to continue...")
Console.ReadLine()
```

Step 8: Save, build, and execute your program so that it works. Paste your code into a Word document.

Lab 3.4 – Programming Challenge – Network Systems Administration

Visual Basic code for the following programming problem that you already logically solved in lab 3.1 and 3.2:

Reread the following program prior to completing the lab.

```
Write a program that will take in basic information from a
student, including their name and how many credits they
have taken in Network Systems Administration program.  The
program will then calculate how many credits are needed to
graduate.  Display should include the student name and the
number of credits left to graduate.  This should be based
off a 90 credit program, where some courses are half
credits.
```

Demo Video: View *lab3-4.wmv* in the Lab 3 folder on the accompanying Lab Demo Media and Startup Files CD.

The Visual Basic Code

Paste your code into a Word document.

Lab 4: Modules

This lab accompanies **Chapter 3** of *Starting Out with Programming Logic & Design*.

Lab 4.1 – Pseudocode and Modules

Critical Review

A Module is a group of statements that exists within a program for the purpose of performing a specific task.

Modules are commonly called procedures, subroutines, subprograms, methods, and functions.

The code for a module is known as a module definition. To execute the module, you write a statement that calls it.

The format for a module definition is as follows:

```
Module name( )
      Statement
      Statement
      Etc.
End Module
```

Calling a module is normally done from the Main ( ) module such as:

```
Call name( )
```

Generally, local variables should be used and arguments should be passed by reference when the value of the variable is changed in the module and needs to be retained. For example:

```
Module main( )
      Real Integer number
      Call inputData(number)
      Call printData(number)
End Module

//accepts number as a reference so the changed value
//will be retained
Module inputData(Real Ref number)
      Number = 20
End Module

//number does not to be sent as a reference because
//number is not going to be modified
Module printData(number)
       Display "The number is ", number
End Module
```

Demo Video: View *lab4-1.wmv* in the Lab 4 folder on the accompanying Lab Demo Media and Startup Files CD

This lab requires you to think about the steps that take place in a program by writing pseudocode. Read the following program prior to completing the lab.

> Data Communications Corp wants a small program that will calculate the cost of UTP it installs for their clients. Write a program that will ask the user to input the name of the client, the number of feet of cable installed. The program should then calculate and display a final bill. Cost per foot of UTP is .21 cents. Be sure to add on a tax of 6%. Final bill should include the total cost and client name. Be sure to add modules to your program.

Consider the following variables and modules in your program. (Reference: Defining and Calling a Module, page 78).

Variable Name
Declare String clientName
Declare Real feetUTP
Declare Real subTotal
Declare Real taxCost
Declare Real totalCost

Module Name
Module inputData ()
Module calcCosts()
Module displayBill()

Step 1: Complete the pseudocode by writing the missing lines. (Reference: Defining and Calling a Module, page 78-81). Also, when writing your modules and making calls, be sure to pass necessary variables as arguments and accept them as reference parameters if they need to be modified in the module. (Reference: Passing Arguments by Value and by Reference, page 97 – 103).

```
Module main ()
      //Declare local variables
      1.
      2.
      3.
      4.
      5.

      //Module calls
      6.
      7.
      8.
```

```
End Module

//this module takes in the required user input.  There will
//be a display and input for each variable
Module inputData(Real Ref feetUTP, String Ref clientName)
     9.
     10.
     11.
     12.
End Module

//this module calculates subTotal, taxCost, and totalCost
//you also need feetUTP passed in to calculate subTotal
Module calcCosts(13.   ,    ,    , )
     14.
     15.
     16.
End Module

//this module displays clientName and totalCost
Module displayBill (17.   ,   )
     18.
     19.
End Module
```

Lab 4.2– Flowcharts and Modules

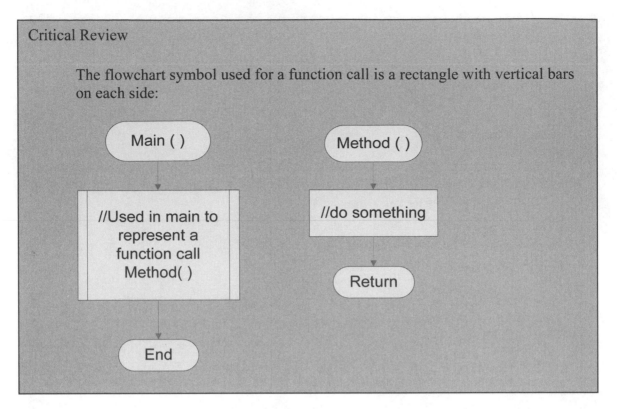

Critical Review

The flowchart symbol used for a function call is a rectangle with vertical bars on each side:

Main ( )

//Used in main to represent a function call Method( )

End

Method ( )

//do something

Return

Demo Video: View *lab4-2.wmv* in the Lab 4 folder on the accompanying Lab Demo Media and Startup Files CD

This lab requires you to think about the steps that take place in a program by designing a flowchart. Use an application such as Raptor or Visio. Read the following program prior to completing the lab.

```
Data Communications Corp wants a small program that will
calculate the cost of UTP it installs for their clients.
Write a program that will ask the user to input the name of
the client, the number of feet of cable installed.  The
program should then calculate and display a final bill.
Cost per foot of UTP is .21 cents.  Be sure to add on a tax
of 6%.  Final bill should include the total cost and client
name.  Be sure to add modules to your program.
```

Step 1: In main, create a module called declareVariables( ) that will set your variables to 0 or " ". Click the Call Symbol on the Left and Drag and Drop to the flow lines between Start and Stop. Double click on the Call Symbol and type the name of your first module. For example, type declareVariables in the Enter Call box. Do not put the ( ) when using Raptor. Click the Done button. A new box will pop up that will ask you to create a new tab. Click Yes. A new tab will be created for your new method.   Notice the new Tab called declareVariables. **Watch the Help Video 4-2 to see how to add modules and initialize variables in Raptor and Visio.**

Step 2: Continue this process to add your additional methods, which are inputData( ), calcCosts( ), and displayBill( ). Main should look like this:

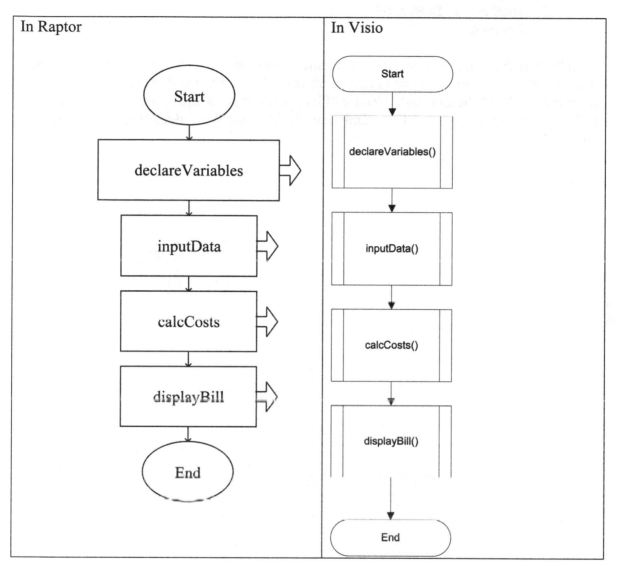

Step 3: Click on the inputData module and add the necessary code to input clientName and feetUTP. **Watch the Help Video 4-2 to see how to input variables in Raptor and Visio.**

Step 4: Click the calcCosts module and add the necessary code to compute calculations. **Watch the Help Video 4-2 to see how to add calculations in Raptor and Visio.**

Step 5: Click the displayBill module and add the necessary code to display the clientName and totalCost to the screen. **Watch the Help Video 4-2 to see how to display variables in Raptor and Visio.**

Step 6: If you are using Raptor, you can run your program. Click Run, then Execute to Finish. For your input, enter a client name such as Bumpco Inc and 3758 feet of cable installed. If your program is coded correctly, the output should be as follows:

> *The clients name is Bumpco Inc*
> *The final cost is $836.5308*
> *----Run complete.*

Step 7: The final step is to insert your finished flowchart into a Word document. Inside Raptor, select File and the Print to Clipboard from the menu. Inside your Word document, select Edit and Paste. You will have to do this for each module you created. In Visio, select Edit and then Copy Drawing. Inside your Word document, select Edit and Paste.

Lab 4.3 – Visual Basic and Modules

Critical Review

To create a module, write its definition. The keyword *Sub* is used before a module name, followed by parentheses. Here is the general format of a function definition in Visual Basic:

```
Sub moduleName( )
    statement
    statement
End Sub
```

Calling a function is done in order to make the module execute. The general format is:

```
ModuleName( )
```

Variables can be passed to modules by using the ByRef or ByVal keywords such as:
```
Sub moduleName(ByRef variable1Name as dataType, ByRef variable2Name as dataType)
```

Demo Video: View *lab4-3.wmv* in the Lab 4 folder on the accompanying Lab Demo Media and Startup Files CD

This lab requires you to write the following program in Visual Basic, console application using modules. Read the following program prior to completing the lab.

```
Data Communications Corp wants a small program that will
calculate the cost of UTP it installs for their clients.
Write a program that will ask the user to input the name of
the client, the number of feet of cable installed.  The
program should then calculate and display a final bill.
Cost per foot of UTP is .21 cents.  Be sure to add on a tax
of 6%.  Final bill should include the total cost and client
name.  Be sure to add modules to your program.
```

Step 1: Start Visual Basic, creating a new Console Application, and save your program. This will automatically add the following:

```
Module Module1

    Sub Main()

    End Sub
```

```
End Module
```

Step 2: Inside Main( ), declare your variables for this program. This should include the following declarations:

```
Dim clientName As String = "NO VALUE"
Dim feetUTP As Double = 0
Dim subTotal As Double = 0
Dim taxCost As Double = 0
Dim totalCost As Double = 0
```

Step 3: After the End Sub command in main, add a new module for inputData( ). This should look like:

```
Sub inputData(ByRef clientName As String, ByRef feetUTP As
Double)
```

The End Sub command will automatically be added. clientName and feetUTP are passed using the ByRef command because you need to retain the value of the variable.

Inside the module, add the following:

```
Console.Write("Enter the clients name: ")
clientName = Console.ReadLine()
Console.Write("Enter the number of feet of UTP installed: ")
feetUTP = Console.ReadLine()
```

This allows the user to enter the necessary data.

Step 4: Below that module, add a new module for calcCosts( ). Pass feetUTP as ByVal, and subTotal, taxCost, and totalCost as ByRef. Inside this module, process your calculations for subTotal, taxCost, and totalCost.

Step 5: Below that module, add a new module for finalBill( ). Pass clientName and totalCost as ByVal. Remember, ByRef is only needed if you are changing the value of a variable in a module. Since we are simply using the value of the variable in this case, ByVal works more efficiently. Inside the module, use Console.WriteLine( ) to display the values of the variables.

Step 6: In main under the variable declarations, add your module calls, passing the appropriate variables such as:

```
inputData(clientName, feetUTP)
calcCosts(feetUTP, subTotal, taxCost, totalCost)
finalBill(clientName, totalCost)

You might also include a pause by adding the following:
Console.Write("Press enter to continue...")
Console.ReadLine()
```

Step 7: Execute your program so that it works and paste the final code below. Sample output might look like:

> *Enter the client's name: Bumpco Inc.*
> *Enter the number of feet of UTP installed: 4593*
> *The client's name is Bumpco Inc.*
> *The final cost is $1022.4018*
> *Press enter to continue...*

Paste your code into a Word document.

Lab 4.4 – Challenge: Ping and Website Launches

Demo Video: View *lab4-4.wmv* in the Lab 4 folder on the accompanying Lab Demo Media and Startup Files CD

This lab requires you to write a Visual Basic program that includes modules to do the following tasks important in the field of networking and programming:

> *What is ping.exe?*
>> *Ping.exe is a simple network utility to test whether or not a device such as a router, server or switch is contactable. When the device receives this information it then sends a reply saying "yes, I am here". Ping is used a lot in IT and network troubleshooting.*
>
> *What is System.Diagnostics.Process.Start( )?*
>> *This is a system function/module built into Visual Basic. This function/module can be used to start a process resource such as launching a website.*

- Write a module called pingMe( ) that will use Ping.exe to get a response from your IP loopback address of 127.0.0.1. This should include the following line of code.
  - ```
    Shell("Ping.exe 127.0.0.1", , True)
    ```
- Write a module called openWebsite( ) that will use a string variable called myTargetURL to launch any website such as www.microsoft.com. This should include the following lines of code.
  - ```
    Dim myTargetURL As String = "http://www.microsoft.com"
    ```
  - ```
    System.Diagnostics.Process.Start(myTargetURL)
    ```
- Write a module called finalOutput( ) that explains what the Shell function does, what ping.exe does, and how you declare variables. Use additional resources to find explanations.
- In main( ), write calls to all three modules.

Your sample output might look as such. Additionally, a web browser should launch displaying the requested website.
    ```

The Visual Basic Code

Paste your completed code into a Word document.

Lab 5: Decisions and Boolean Logic I
This lab accompanies **Chapter 4 (pp. 115-142 and 147-155)** of *Starting Out with Programming Logic & Design*.

Lab 5.1 – Evaluating Conditions with Relational Operators

Critical Review

A relational operator determines whether a specific relationship exists between two values.

Relational operators

Operator	Meaning	Boolean Expression
>	Greater than	X > Y
<	Less than	X < Y
>=	Greater than or equal to	X >= Y
<=	Less than or equal to	X <= Y
==	Equal to	X == Y
!=	Not equal to	X != Y

Demo Video: View *lab5-1.wmv* **in the Lab 5 folder on the accompanying Lab Demo Media and Startup Files CD**

This lab requires you to think about possible true and false conditions using if statements.

Step 1: Consider the following values set to variables for average download speeds in kbps for mobile data carriers.
- attAverage = 1410
- sprintAverage = 795
- tmobileAverage = 868
- verizonAverage = 877

Step 2: Based on the values to the variables in Step 1, do the following conditions result in a true or false statement? (Reference: Relational Operators, page 119).

The condition	True or False
attAverage >= verizonAverage	
tmobileAverage == 868	
verizonAverage < sprintAverage	
sprintAverage != attAverage	

Lab 5.2 – Evaluating Conditions with Logical Operators

Critical Review

The logical AND operator and the logical OR operator allow you to connect multiple expressions to create a compound expression.

The logical NOT operator reverses the truth of an expression.

When using the AND operator, both conditions must be true in order for the statements within an if to process.

When using the OR operator, either condition must be true in order for the statements within an if to process.

Demo Video: View *lab5-2.wmv* in the Lab 5 folder on the accompanying Lab Demo Media and Startup Files CD (note lab reference in video is incorrect)

This lab requires you to think about possible true and false conditions using if statements.

Step 1: Consider the following values set to variables for average download speeds in kbps for mobile data carriers.
- attAverage = 1410
- sprintAverage = 795
- tmobileAverage = 868
- verizonAverage = 877

Step 2: Based on the values to the variables in Step 1, what is the expected output? (Reference: Logical Operators, page 147).

The condition	Expected Output

If tmobileAverage > 800 AND verizonAverage > 800 Then
   Display "Both have average download rates over 800"
Else
   Display "One or both of the averages are less"
End If	

If sprintAverage == 800 Then
   Display "Sprints download rate is 800"
End If	

If attAverage >= 1300 OR tmobileAverage >=900 Display "Select either carrier" End If	

Lab 5.3 – Pseudocode

Critical Review

> Questions are often asked using an if statement such as if (X > Y), whereas the question asked is "is X greater than Y"?
>
> The general structure of an if statement is
> ```
> If condition Then
>       Statement
>       Statement
>       Etc.
> End If
> ```
>
> A dual alternative decision structure will execute one group of statements if its Boolean expression is true, or another group if its Boolean expression is false.
>
> The general structure of an if then else statement is
> ```
>       If condition Then
>             Statement
>             Statement
>             Etc.
>       Else
>             Statement
>             Statement
>             Etc.
>       End If
> ```
>
> **Demo Video: View *lab5-3.wmv* in the Lab 5 folder on the accompanying Lab Demo Media and Startup Files CD**

This lab requires you to think about the steps that take place in a program by writing pseudocode. Read the following program prior to completing the lab.

```
Career Tech Placement is hiring employees for placement at
technology firms across the city.  Prior to granting an
interview, they have a 100 point test that the will use to
determine if the candidate should be interviewed.
Depending on their score, they get placed in 1 of 4
categories for possible employment and flag for an
interview:
```

Score	Employment Category	Interview Possibility
85 or above	Definite	Yes
70 – 84	Likely	Yes
60 – 69	Maybe	Yes
59 or below	No	No

```
They have asked you to write a program that will allow them
to enter a test score and then set the employment category
```

```
and the interview possibility variables based on the chart
above.
```

Given the major task involved in this program, you decide your program should have three variables and three modules:

Variable Name	Purpose
`Declare Integer testScore = 0`	Stores the test score of the candidate.
`Declare String category = " "`	Stores Definite, Likely, Maybe, or No
`Declare String interview = " "`	Stores Yes or No

Module Name	Purpose
`Module getScore()`	Allows the user to enter the test score
`Module employCat()`	Determines the employment category
`Module interviewPoss()`	This module will determine if a day off should be awarded.
`Module displayInfo()`	Displays the testScore, category, and interview variables.

Step 1: Complete the pseudocode by writing the missing lines. When writing your modules and making calls, be sure to pass necessary variables as arguments and accept them as reference parameters if they need to be modified in the module. (Reference: Testing a Series of Conditions, page 138).

Main Module( )
    //Declare variables on the next 3 lines

    //Make Module calls and pass necessary variables on the next 4 lines

End Main

Module getScore(Integer Ref testScore)
    //Ask the user to enter a test score

End Module

Module employCat(Integer testScore, String Ref category)
    //Determine what employment category they are in based on their test score
    //Similar to if the score is less than 60, then category is "No"
        //Otherwise, if score is less than 70 then category is "Maybe"
            //…and so on

End Module

Module interviewPoss(Integer testScore, String Ref interview)
      //Determine if they qualify for an interview based on their test score
      //Similar to if the score is less than 60, then interview is "No"
            //Otherwise, interview is "Yes"

End Module

Module displayInfo(Integer testScore, String category, String interview)
      //Display the three variables

End Module

Lab 5.4 – Flowcharts

Critical Review

The flowchart symbol used to indicate some condition is a diamond. An if statement is called a single alternative decision structure. The code will only process if the decision is true.

A dual alternative decision structure has two possible paths of execution – one path is taken if a condition is true, and the other path is taken if the condition is false.

A diamond with a true and false value is used in flowcharting a dual alternative decision structure.

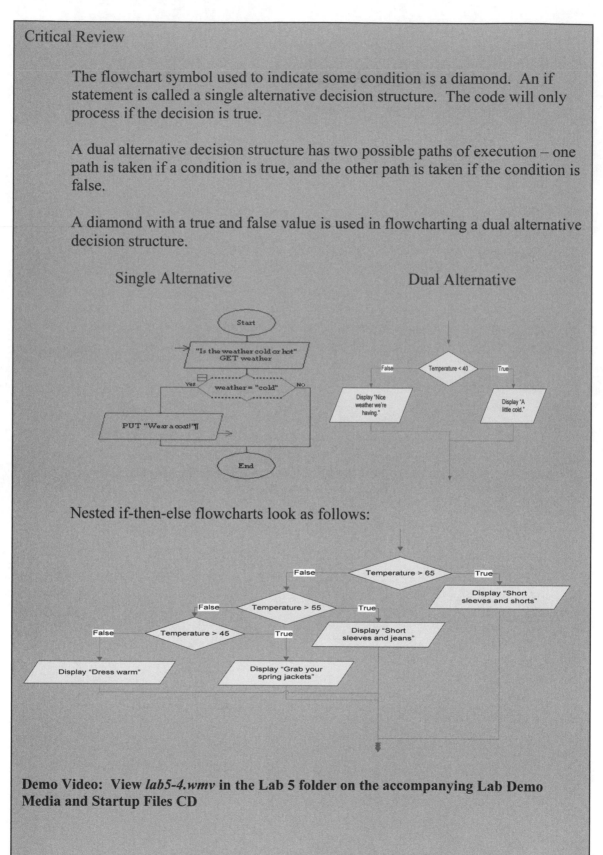

Nested if-then-else flowcharts look as follows:

Demo Video: View *lab5-4.wmv* in the Lab 5 folder on the accompanying Lab Demo Media and Startup Files CD

This lab requires you to convert your pseudocode in Lab 5.3 to a flowchart. Use an application such as Raptor or Visio.

Step 1: Launch Raptor or Visio and convert your pseudocode from Lab 5.3 into a flowchart. Depending on which application you are using, select either *lab5-3raptor.rap* or *lab5-3visio.vsd* from the Lab 5 folder on the accompanying Lab Demo Media and Startup Files CD to get started. **Once you double click on them to open, do a Save As to save it to your workspace.** Watch the demo video 5-4 for help. **(note file numbers are incorrect)**

Step 2: The final step is to insert your finished flowchart into a Word document. Inside Raptor, select File and the Print to Clipboard from the menu. If you are using Visio, select Edit, then Select All, then Edit and Copy. In your Word document, select Edit and Paste.

Lab 5.5 – Visual Basic

Critical Review

In Visual Basic, we use the If, or If Then ElseIf to write a single or dual alternative decision structure.

Here is the general format of the If Then ElseIf statement:

```
If testScore < 60 Then
      category = "No"
    ElseIf testScore < 70 Then
      category = "Maybe"
    ElseIf testScore < 85 Then
      category = "Likely"
    Else
      category = "Definite"
    End If
```

Here is the general format of the If Then Else statement:

```
    If testScore < 60 Then
      interview = "No"
    Else
      interview = "Yes"
    End If
```

Visual Basic will automatically add the Then, and End If and format the structure.

Demo Video: View *lab5-5.wmv* in the Lab 5 folder on the accompanying Lab Demo Media and Startup Files CD

This lab requires you to convert the pseudocode and flowchart into an actual program using Visual Basic.

Step 1: Launch Visual Basic and create a new Console Application. Save it to the appropriate location.

Step 2: We will be using Modules in this program so all variables and module calls will go between of Sub Main( ) and End Sub. In VB, start by declaring and initializing your variables and making module calls such as:

```
Sub Main()
    'declare your 3 variables similar format such as
    'Dim variableName As DataType = 0 (or " " if it's a string)
```

```
        'call your 4 modules and pass necessary variables similar
        'format such as
        'moduleName(arguments)




        'add this to cause a pause
        Console.WriteLine("Press enter to continue...")
        Console.ReadLine()
    End Sub
```

Step 3: Code the getScore( ) module so that the user enters a test score. Remember to use ByRef so the value of testScore is retained. This module will look like:

```
    Sub getScore(ByRef testScore As Integer)
      'add the code to input testScore

    End Sub
```

Step 4: Code the employCat( ) module that will determine the category placement. Remember to use ByRef so the value of category is retained. This module will look like:

```
    Sub employCat(byVal testScore as Integer, byRef category as String)
        'add the code to evaluate conditions
        If testScore < 60 Then
            category = "No"
        ElseIf testScore < 70 Then
            category = "Maybe"
        ElseIf testScore < 85 Then
            category = "Likely"
        Else
            category = "Definite"
        End If
    End Sub
```

Step 5: Code the interviewPoss( ) module that will determine the interview value. Use ByRef for interview, and byVal for testScore. This will be a simple If Then Else that will set the interview variable to either "Yes" or "No".

Step 6: Code the displayInfo( ) module and use Console.WriteLine( ) to display the values of the three variables. All three variables can be passed as ByVal.

Step 7: Save, build, and execute your program so that it works. Paste your code into a Word document.

Lab 6: Decisions and Boolean Logic II
This lab accompanies **Chapter 4 (pp. 142-147)** of *Starting Out with Programming Logic & Design*.

Lab 6.1 – Pseudocode

Critical Review

Case Structures
A case structure lets the value of a variable or expressions determine which path of execution the program will take. This is often used as an alternative to a nested if else decision. The general syntax is:

Select testExpression
    Case 1:
        Statement...
    Case 2:
        Statement...
    Case 3:
        Statement...
    Insert as many cases as necessary
End Select

Logical Operators
The logical *AND*, *OR*, or *NOT* allow multiple expressions to be connected.

Boolean Variables
Boolean variables hold either a true or false value. The data type is Boolean and can be changed to True or False throughout a program such has:

Declare Boolean isHungry
If eatTime > 12 then
    Set isHungry – False
Else
    Set isHungry = True
End If

Demo Video: View *lab6-1.wmv* in the Lab 6 folder on the accompanying Lab Demo Media and Startup Files CD

This lab requires you to write pseudocode based on the following flowcharts:

Step 1: Convert this module called inputOptions( ) to pseudocode that includes an if else statement and variables that have already been declared in main as follows:

```
Declare Integer mobileProvider = 0
Declare Integer dataOption = 0
```

Declare Boolean dataPackage = True

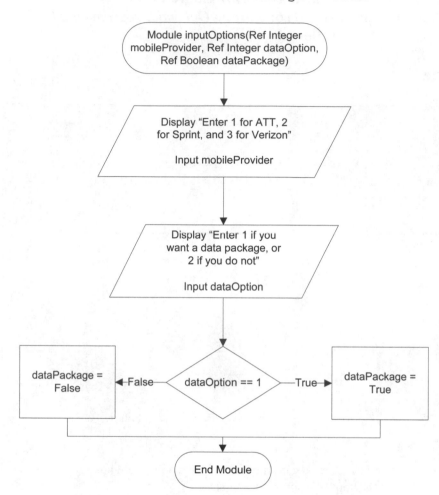

Module inputOptions(//PASS IN VARIABLES AS REFERENCES)
        //TYPE CODE HERE

End Module

Step 2: Convert this module called displayProvider( ) to a case structure in pseudocode based on the variable mobileProvider. It is currently flowcharted as a nested if else statement. (Reference page 142, The Case Structure).

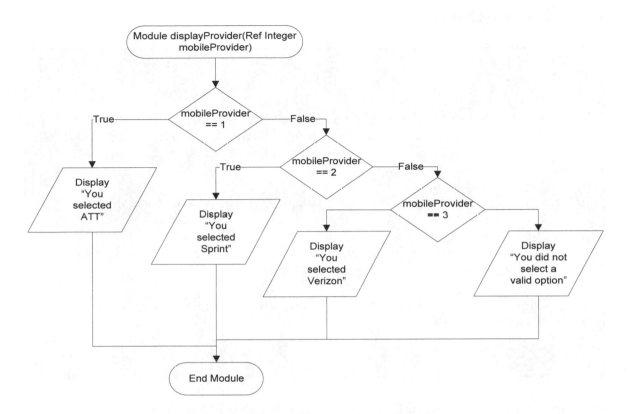

```
Module displayProvider(//PASS IN VARIABLE AS REFERENCES)
        //FINISH CODE HERE
        Select mobileProvider
                Case 1:



End Module
```

Step 3: Convert this algorithm to a nested if else decision using logical operators:

1. Get mobileProvider (1 for ATT, 2 for Sprint, or 3 for Verizon).
2. Get dataOption (1 for data package or 2 for no data package).
3. Set dataPackage to True or False.
4. If mobileProvider is equal to 1 AND dataPackage is equal to True, then display they have selected ATT with a Data Package.
5. Else if mobileProvider is equal to 2 OR dataPackage is equal to True, then display they have selected Sprint or they have selected with a Data Package.
6. Else if mobileProvider is equal to 3 AND dataPackage is equal to False, then display they have selected Verizon and No Data Package.

```
//Start nested if else below
```

Lab 6.2 – Flowcharts

Critical Review

Case Structures
A case structure lets the value of a variable or expressions determine which path of execution the program will take. This is often used as an alternative to a nested if else decision. See p. 143, The Case Structure for a flowchart example.

Logical Operators
The logical *AND*, *OR*, or *NOT* allow multiple expressions to be connected.

Boolean Variables
Boolean variables hold either a true or false value. The data type is Boolean and can be changed to True or False throughout a program.

Demo Video: View *lab6-2.wmv* in the Lab 6 folder on the accompanying Lab Demo Media and Startup Files CD

This lab requires you to convert your pseudocode in Lab 6.1 to a flowchart as a complete program. Use an application such as Visio. Raptor does not allow for Case Structure, only nested if else decisions.

Step 1: Launch Visio and complete the Visio skeleton into a complete flowchart. Select *lab6-3visio.vsd* from the Lab 6 folder on the accompanying Lab Demo Media and Startup Files CD to get started. **Once you double click on it to open, do a Save As to save it to your workspace.** Watch the demo video 6.2 for help.

Step 2: In the Main Module( ), start by adding the three variables:

```
Declare Integer mobileProvider = 0
Declare Integer dataOption = 0
Declare Boolean dataPackage = True
```

Step 3: In the Main Module( ), add the three module calls, passing the appropriate variables into the modules:

```
Call inputOptions(//...add variables to match headers)
Call displayProvider(//...add variables to match headers)
Call displayChoices(//...add variables to match headers)
```

Step 4: Finish adding the flow lines to the Main Module. Note that inputOptions( ) is already coded and complete.

Step 5: Next, complete the displayProvider( ) module by converting your pseudocode from lab 6.2, step 2 into a Case Structure. Be sure to add case labels and flow lines.

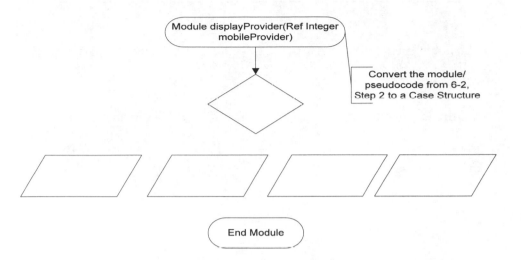

Step 6: Next, complete the displayChoices( ) module by converting the algorithm steps 4, 5 and 6 from lab 6.2 using logical operators in the conditions. Be sure to add flow lines and flow line labels.

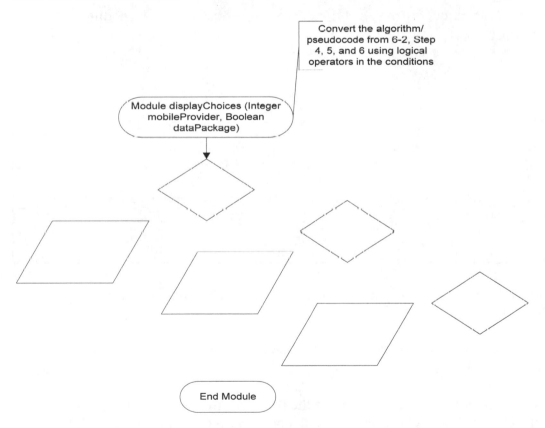

Step 7: The final step is to insert your finished flowchart into a Word document. Inside Visio, select Edit, then Select All, then Edit and Copy. In your Word document, select Edit and Paste.

Lab 6.3 – Visual Basic Programming Challenge

Critical Review

Boolean is the data type to store a true or false value in VB. The syntax is:

```
dim dataPackage as Boolean = True
```

Select Case is the keyword to code a case structure in VB. The general syntax is:

```
Select Case variableName
     Case 1
          'statements
     Case 2
          'statements
     Case 3
          'statements
     Case Else
          'statements
  End Select
```

Logical Operators or And and Or will be used in this lab. Each condition needs to be processed individually such as:

```
if mobileProvider = 1 and dataPackage = True then
   'do something
ElseIf '...

End If
```

Relational Operator == is just one = equal sign in VB.

Demo Video: View *lab6-3.wmv* in the Lab 6 folder on the accompanying Lab Demo Media and Startup Files CD

This lab requires you to convert the pseudocode and flowchart into an actual program using Visual Basic.

Step 1: Launch Visual Basic and create a new Console Application. Save it to the appropriate location.

Step 2: Using the following skeleton, code the flowchart from 6.2 in Visual Basic. Review the Critical Review section to learn to code a Select Case, Boolean variables, and Logical Operators. **Also note that the == double equal sign in pseudocode and flowcharts is just one = equal sign in VB.** You may copy the following and replace the code that is in your empty workspace.

```vb
Module Module1

Sub Main()
    'declare and initialize 3 variables
    Dim dataPackage As Boolean = True 'how boolean variables are
declared

    'call 3 modules and pass appropriate variables

    'the pause
    Console.WriteLine("Press any key to continue...")
    Console.ReadLine()

End Sub

Sub inputOptions('pass in variables with appropriate data type and
byRef or byVal)
    'take in values for the 2 variables and write an if else to set
dataPackage to True or False

End Sub

Sub displayProvider('pass in variable with appropriate data type
and byRef or byVal)
    'write a case structure to display what they selected based on
the flowchart
    'review the Critical Review section to see how a Select Case
structure is used in VB

End Sub

Sub displayChoices('pass in variables with appropriate data type
and byRef or byVal)
    'write nested if else statement with logical operators based on
the flowchart
    'review the Critical Review section to see how to use logical
operators with a nested if else in VB

End Sub

End Module
```

Step 3: Save, build, and execute your program so that it works. Paste your code into a Word document.

Lab 7: Repetition Structures I
This lab accompanies **Chapter 5 (pp. 163-183 and pp. 196-201)** of *Starting Out with Programming Logic & Design.*

Lab 7.1 – Condition Controlled with While and Do-While Loops: Pseudocode

Critical Review

A repetition structure causes a statement or set of statements to execute repeatedly.

Repetition structures are used to perform the same task over and over.

Repetition structures are commonly called loops.

A condition-controlled loop uses a true/false condition to control the number of times that it repeats.

The general structure of a While loop with a condition-controlled statement is:

```
//Declare loop control variable
While condition
     Statement
     Statement
     Etc.
     //Ask Question that changes the loop control variable
End While
```

The general structure of a Do While loop with a condition-controlled statement is:

```
//Declare loop control variable
Do
     Statement
     Statement
     Etc.
     //Ask Question that changes the loop control variable
While Condition
```

Demo Video: View *lab7-1.wmv* in the Lab 7 folder on the accompanying Lab Demo Media and Startup Files CD

Step 1: Examine the following pseudocode main module from Lab 4.1. Loops are commonly used to call modules multiple times. The best design is to use a loop around the module calls in Main.

```
Module main ()
      //Declare local variables
      Declare String clientName = " "
      Declare Real feetUTP = 0
      Declare Real subTotal = 0
      Declare Real taxCost = 0
      Declare Real totalCost = 0

      //Module calls
      Call inputData(feetUTP, clientName)
      Call calcCosts(feetUTP, subTotal, taxCost, totalCost)
      Call displayBill(clientName, totalCost)

End Module
```

Step 2: In the space provided, re-write the pseudocode for the main module with a condition controlled While or a Do-While loop so that the program runs multiple times. Create a loop control variable named keepGoing of the data type string and initialize this variable to "y". Don't forget to indent the contents of your loop. (Reference: Modularizing the Code in the Body of a Loop, page 172).

Lab 7.2 – Condition Controlled with While and Do-While Loops: Flowcharts

Critical Review

In a while loop, the question is asked first. After the statements process, the control goes back above the condition.

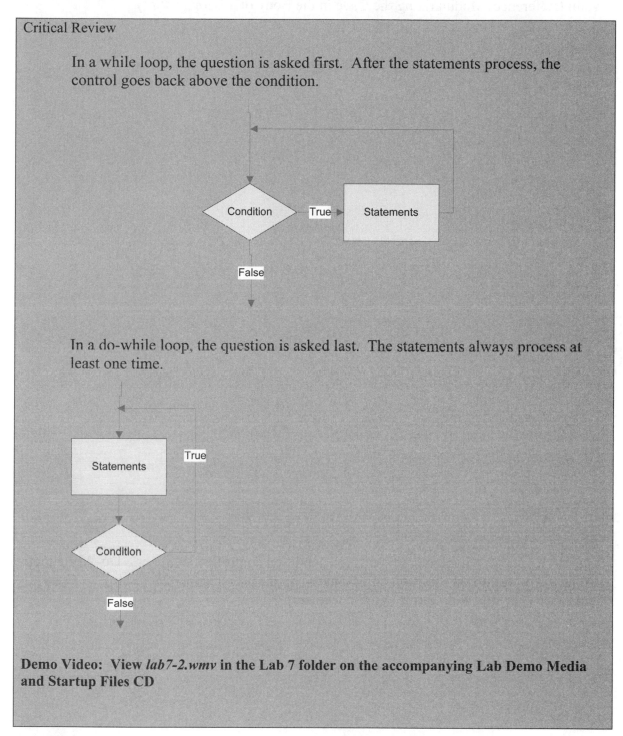

In a do-while loop, the question is asked last. The statements always process at least one time.

Demo Video: View *lab7-2.wmv* in the Lab 7 folder on the accompanying Lab Demo Media and Startup Files CD

Step 1: Examine the following main module from Lab 4.2. Loops are commonly used to call modules multiple times. The best design is to use a loop around the module calls in Main (Reference: Modularizing the Code in the Body of a Loop, p. 173).

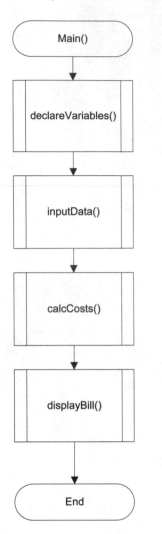

Step 2: Redesign the main module with a condition controlled While or a Do-While loop so that the program runs multiple times, based on the pseudocode from Lab 7-1. Copy and paste your flowchart into a Word document.

Lab 7.3 – Count Controlled with While and Do-While Loops: Pseudocode

Critical Review

A count-controlled loop repeats a specific number of times.

The loop keeps a count of the number of times that it iterates, and when the count reaches a specified amount, the loop stops.

A variable, known as a counter variable, is used to store the number of iterations that it has performed.

The three actions that take place are initialization, test, and increment.
- Initialization: Before the loop begins, the counter variable is initialized to a starting value.
- Test: The loop tests the counter variable by comparing it to a maximum value.
- Increment: To increment a variable means to increase its value. This is done by adding one to the loop control variable.

Any loop can be used with a count-controlled loop.

The general structure of a While loop (although it is the same process with a Do-While loop) with a count-controlled statement is:

```
//Declare loop control variable
Declare Integer counter = 1
While condition
      Statement
      Statement
      Etc.
      //increment counter
      Set counter - counter + 1
End While
```

Demo Video: View *lab7-3.wmv* in the Lab 7 folder on the accompanying Lab Demo Media and Startup Files CD

Step 1: Understanding how to raise a number to the power of 2 is very important to the field of networking as it relates to binary conversion. Convert the following algorithm to pseudocode using a count controlled do while or while loop:

1. Create three integer variables called toPower, number, and counter. Set counter to 0, and toPower and number to 2.
2. Write a do while loop or while loop that will run 7 iterations.
3. Inside the loop, set toPower equal to 2 to the power of the number variable.

4. Display "2 to the power of", number, " is", toPower to the screen.
5. Increment counter and number by 1.

Copy and paste your pseudocode into a Word document.

Lab 7.4 –Count Controlled with While and Do-While Loops: Flowcharts

Critical Review

In a count controlled while or do-while loop, the flowchart is essentially the same as a condition controlled, except you must create a counter and manually increment the counter variable. The general flow using a while loop looks as follows:

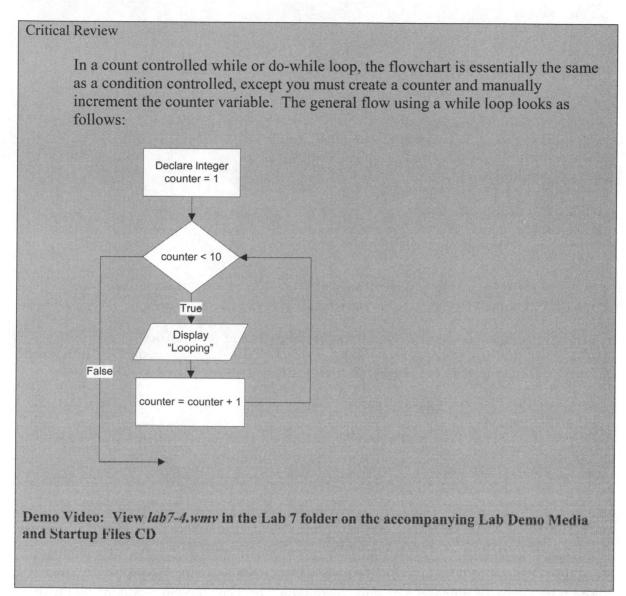

Demo Video: View *lab7-4.wmv* in the Lab 7 folder on the accompanying Lab Demo Media and Startup Files CD

Step 1: Using your pseudocode from lab 7-3, design either a while or a do while loop of raising 2 to the power of 2-8 to the screen.

Copy and paste your flowchart into a Word document.

Lab 7.5 –While and Do While Loops: Visual Basic Challenge I

Critical Review

Visual Basic supports both While and Do While loops. The general syntax for a condition controlled loop is as follows:

While loop:

```
While keepGoing = "yes"

End While
```

Do While loop:

```
Do While keepGoing = "yes"

Loop
```

Visual Basic will automatically end your While with an End While, and end your Do While with the Loop.

Count controlled loops are structured the same way, but you must declare a counter variable as an Integer as loops only count in whole increments. Additionally, do not forget to increment or decrement your counter variable.

Demo Video: View *lab7-5.wmv* in the Lab 7 folder on the accompanying Lab Demo Media and Startup Files CD

Write either the Pseudocode OR Flowchart AND the Visual Basic Code

Design a program that will use your pingMe( ) module from Lab 4-4. There should be a condition controlled loop in Main to run the program multiple times if the user wants. Additionally, in the pingMe( ) module, there should be a count controlled loop that will ping your system after a count down of 5 (Reference p. 199, Decrementing). You may use while or do while loops. Your output may look as follows:

```
c:\  file:///C:/Documents and Settings/Staff/Desktop/ITT Lab Manual/Lab 7/work files/lab7-5vb/l...  _ □ ×
Count down ...5
Count down ...4
Count down ...3
Count down ...2
Count down ...1
Now Ping....

Pinging 127.0.0.1 with 32 bytes of data:

Reply from 127.0.0.1: bytes=32 time<1ms TTL=128
Reply from 127.0.0.1: bytes=32 time<1ms TTL=128
Reply from 127.0.0.1: bytes=32 time<1ms TTL=128
Reply from 127.0.0.1: bytes=32 time<1ms TTL=128

Ping statistics for 127.0.0.1:
    Packets: Sent = 4, Received = 4, Lost = 0 (0% loss),
Approximate round trip times in milli-seconds:
    Minimum = 0ms, Maximum = 0ms, Average = 0ms

Enter yes if you want to run program again: _
```

Copy and paste your flowchart OR pseudocode into a Word document.

Copy and paste your Visual Basic code into a Word document.

Lab 7.6 –While and Do While Loops: Visual Basic Challenge II

Based on Lab 7-3 and 7-4, code the flowchart/pseudocode by converting 2 to the power of a number from 2 to 8. You should have a main module that calls a module called displayPower( ) as many times as the user types yes (using a condition controlled loop). The displayPower( ) module should use a count controlled loop that raises the toPower variable to 2 to the power of the number, such as `toPower = 2 ^ number`. The output should look as:

```
file:///C:/Documents and Settings/Staff/Desktop/ITT Lab Manual/Lab 7/work files/lab7-6/lab...
2 to the power of 2 is 4
2 to the power of 3 is 8
2 to the power of 4 is 16
2 to the power of 5 is 32
2 to the power of 6 is 64
2 to the power of 7 is 128
2 to the power of 8 is 256
Do you want to run again yes or no: yes
2 to the power of 2 is 4
2 to the power of 3 is 8
2 to the power of 4 is 16
2 to the power of 5 is 32
2 to the power of 6 is 64
2 to the power of 7 is 128
2 to the power of 8 is 256
Do you want to run again yes or no: no
Press enter to continue...
```

Demo Video: View *lab7-6.wmv* in the Lab 7 folder on the accompanying Lab Demo Media and Startup Files CD

Copy and paste your Visual Basic code into a Word document.

Lab 8: Repetition Structures II
This lab accompanies **Chapter 5 (pp. 183-195 and pp. 201-211)** of *Starting Out with Programming Logic & Design*.

Lab 8.1 – For Loop and Accumulation with Pseudocode

Critical Review

A count-controlled loop iterates a specific number of times. Although you can write this with a while or a do-while loop, most programming languages provide a loop known as the for loop. This loop is specifically designed as a count-controlled loop.

The process of the for loop is:
- The loop keeps a count of the number of times that it iterates, and when the count reaches a specified amount, the loop stops.
- A count-controlled loop uses a variable known as a counter variable to store the number of iterations that it has performed.
- Using the counter, the following three actions take place (Initialization, Test, and Increment).

The pseudocode for a for statement looks as follows:

```
For counterVariable = startingValue to maxValue
     Statement
     Statement
     Statement
     Etc.
End For
```

A running total is a sum of numbers that accumulates with each iteration of a loop. The variable used to keep the running total is called an accumulator.

Demo Video: View *lab8-1.wmv* in the Lab 8 folder on the accompanying Lab Demo Media and Startup Files CD

This lab requires you to implement a count-controlled loop using a for loop.

Step 1: Examine the following code.

```
Constant Integer MAX_HOURS = 24
Declare Integer hours

For hours = 1 to MAX_HOURS
     Display "The hour is ", hours
End For
```

Step 2: Explain what you think will be displayed to the screen in Step 1. (Reference: For loop, page 186):

_____

_____

_____

Step 3: Write a for loop that will print 60 minutes to the screen. Complete the missing lines of code.

```
Constant Integer MAX_MINUTES = _____
Declare Integer minutes

For _____ = 1 to _____
      Display _____
End For
```

Step 4: Write a for loop that will print 60 seconds to the screen. Complete the missing lines of code.

```
Constant Integer MAX_SECONDS = _____
Declare Integer seconds

For _____ = 1 to _____
      Display _____
End For
```

Step 5: For loops can also be used to increment by more than one. Examine the following code.

```
Constant Integer MAX_VALUE = 10
Declare Integer counter

For counter = 0 to MAX_VALUE Step 2
      Display "The number is ", counter
End For
```

Step 6: Explain what you think will be displayed to the screen in Step 5. (Reference: Incrementing by Values Other than 1, page 190):

_____

_____

_____

Step 7: Write a for loop that will display the numbers starting at 20, then 40, then 60, and continuing the sequence all the way to 200.

```
Constant Integer MAX_VALUE = _____
Declare Integer counter
```

```
For counter = _____ to MAX_VALUE Step _____
      Display "The number is ", _____
End For
```

Step 8: For loops can also be used when the user controls the number of iterations. Examine the following code:

```
Declare Integer numStudents
Declare Integer counter

Display "Enter the number of students in class"
Input numStudents

For counter = 1 to numStudents
      Display "Student #", counter
End For
```

Step 9: Explain what you think will be displayed to the screen in Step 8. (Reference: Letting the User Control the Number of Iterations, page 194):

_____

_____

_____

Step 10: For loops are also commonly used to calculate a running total (accumulation). Examine the following code.

```
Declare Integer counter
Declare Integer total = 0
Declare Integer number

For counter = 1 to 5
      Display "Enter a number: "
      Input number
      Set total = total + number
End For

Display "The total is: ", total
```

Step 11: Explain what you think will be displayed to the screen in Step 10. (Reference: Calculating a Running Total, page 201):

_____

_____

_____

Step 12: Write the missing lines for a program that will allow the user to enter how many ages they want to enter and then find the average.

```
Declare Integer counter
```

```
Declare Integer totalAge = 0
Declare Real averageAge = 0
Declare Integer age
Declare Integer number

Display "How many ages do you want to enter: "
Input _____

For counter = 1 to number
    Display "Enter age: "
    Input _____
    Set totalAge = _____  +  _____
End For

averageAge = _____  /  _____

Display "The average age is ", _____
```

Lab 8.2 – For Loop and Accumulation with Flowcharts

Critical Review

A flowchart for a for loop is similar to that of a while loop, where a condition controls the iterations. Here is an example of a for loop using a flowcharting tool such as Visio.

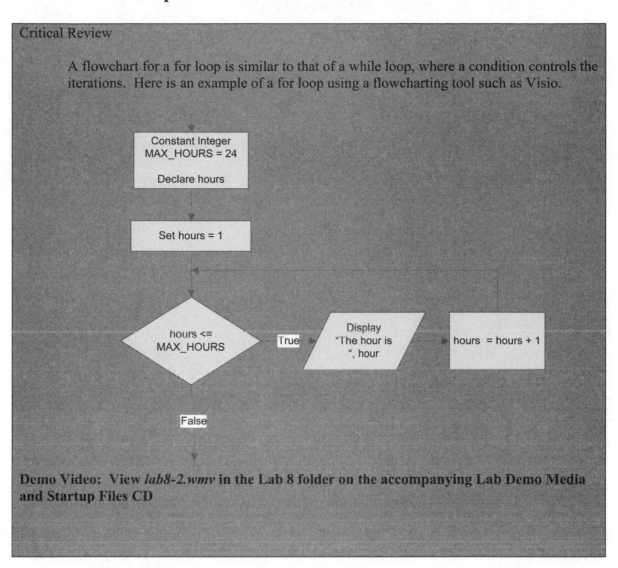

Demo Video: View *lab8-2.wmv* in the Lab 8 folder on the accompanying Lab Demo Media and Startup Files CD

This lab requires you to convert various pseudocode steps in Lab 8.1 to a flowchart. Use an application such as Raptor or Visio.

The Accumulator
Step 1: Launch Raptor or Visio and convert the following pseudocode to a flowchart.

```
Declare Integer counter =1
Declare Integer total = 0
Declare Integer number = 0

For counter = 1 to 5
     Display "Enter a number: "
     Input number
     Set total = total + number
End For
```

```
Display "The total is total: ", total
```

Step 2: Paste your finished flowchart into a Word document.

The Average Age

Step 1: Launch Raptor or Visio and convert the following pseudocode to a flowchart.

```
Declare Integer counter =1
Declare Integer totalAge = 0
Declare Real averageAge = 0
Declare Integer age =0
Declare Integer number =0

Display "How many ages do you want to enter: "
Input number

For counter = 1 to number
     Display "Enter age: "
     Input age
     Set totalAge = totalAge + age
End For

averageAge = totalAge / number

Display "The average age is ", averageAge
```

Step 2: Paste your finished flowchart into a Word document.

Lab 8.3 –Accumulation and Loops: Visual Basic Challenge

Critical Review

Visual Basic supports a For Next and a For Each loop with the general format as such:

```
For counter As Integer = 1 To 5
    Console.WriteLine("in loop")
Next
```

Demo Video: View *lab8-3.wmv* **in the Lab 8 folder on the accompanying Lab Demo Media and Startup Files CD**

Write the Visual Basic code for the following programming problem:

```
Write a program that will allow your manager to easily
calculate the average speed of your network over an 8 hour
work day.  The manager can enter the speed in Mbps each
hour.  Your program will then calculate the average speed
and print out the results.  You must use loops, modules,
and allow your program to run multiple times for different
days to be calculated.
```

Your sample output might look as follows:

You may use the following rough pseudocode to help you code your VB program:

```
Module main()
        //Declare local variables
        Declare anotherDay loop control variable and set to "yes"
        //Loop to run program again
        While anotherDay == "yes"
                //declare and initialize variables
                Declare variables for totalSpeed and averageSpeed

                //calls modules
                Call enterSpeeds(totalSpeed)
                Call calcAverage(totalSpeed, averageSpeed)
                Call displayAverage(averageSpeed)
                Display "Enter yes if you want to calculate another day:"
                Input anotherDay

        End While
End Module

Module enterSpeeds(Double byRef totalSpeed)
        Declare local variables networkSpeed as Double = 0 and counter as Integer = 1

        For loop that runs 8 times
                Take in networkSpeed
                Accumulate totalSpeed as totalSpeed = totalSpeed + networkSpeed
        End for
End Module

Module calcAverage(Double ByVal totalSpeed, Double ByRef averageSpeed)
        Calculate the average as totalSpeed / 8
End Module

Module displayAverage(Double ByVal averageSpeed)
        Display the averageSpeed
End Module
```

Copy and paste Visual Basic code into a Word document.

Lab 9: Functions and Input Validation
This lab accompanies **Chapter 6, "Functions", pp. 217-251 and Chapter 7, "Input Validation", pp. 257-266** of *Starting Out with Programming Logic & Design*.

Lab 9.1 – Functions in Pseudocode and Visual Basic

Critical Review

Your modules in pseudocode can be made into functions by returning a value.

A function is a special type of module that returns a value back to the part of the program that called it.

Most programming languages provide a library of prewritten functions that perform commonly needed tasks.

Library functions are built into the programming language and you can call them as needed. They are commonly performed tasks.

Demo Video: View *lab9 -1.wmv* **in the Lab 9 folder on the accompanying Lab Demo Media and Startup Files CD**

Writing Your Own Function that Returns an Integer
Step 1: A function contains three parts: a header, a body, and a return statement. The first is a function header which specifies the data type of the value that is to be returned, the name of the function, and any parameter variables used by the function to accept arguments. The body is comprised of one or more statements that are executed when the function is called. In the following space, complete the following: (Reference: Writing Your Own Functions, page 225).

a. Write a function with the header named addTen.
b. The function will accept an Integer variable named number.
c. The function body will ask the user to enter a number and the add 10 to the number. The answer will be stored in the variable number.
d. The return statement will return the value of number.

```
Function a._____    a._____    (b._____)
      Display "Enter a number:"
      Input c._____
      Set c._____ = number + 10
Return d._____
```

Step 2: In the following space, write a function call to your function from Step 1.

```
Set number = _____ (_____)
```

Step 3: Launch and create a new workspace in Visual Basic. Place the following code inside and run the program. Notice there is already a call to addTen(number) and that the function call operates the same ways a module call, **except that a function call accepts a returned value.** Therefore, the function call looks as **number = addTen(number).**

```
Module Module1

    Sub Main()

        Dim number As Integer = 0
        number = addTen(number)

        Console.WriteLine("The number with 10 added to it is : "
& number)

        Console.WriteLine("Press any key to continue...")
        Console.ReadLine()

    End Sub


    End Module
```

Step 4: After End Sub in Main( ), add a function by typing the following:

```
Function addTen(ByVal number As Integer)
```

When you hit enter, the `End Function` will automatically be added. All code in the function will be between Function and End Function.

Step 5: Write a line of code that will allow the user to enter a number and then add the formula number = number + 10 based on the pseudocode in step 1 of this lab.

Step 6: Before End Function, add a return statement that looks like:

```
Return number
```

Step 7: Run your program so that it works properly, and then copy and paste your code into a Word document.

Your output might look as follows:

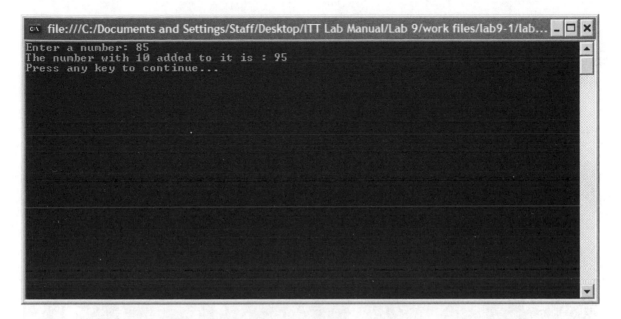

Using Mathematical Library Function: sqrt

Step 8: The sqrt function accepts an argument and returns the square root of the argument.   In the following space, complete the following: (Reference: The sqrt Function, page 240).

   a.   Declare a variable named myNumber and a variable named squareRoot of the data type Real.
   b.   Ask the user to enter a number of which they want to find the square root. Store the input in myNumber.
   c.   Call the sqrt function to determine the square root of myNumber.
   d.   Display the square root to the screen.

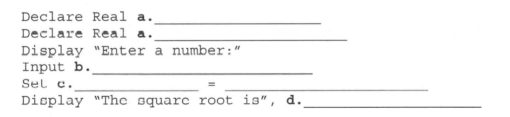

```
Declare Real a._____
Declare Real a._____
Display "Enter a number:"
Input b._____
Set c._____  =  _____
Display "The square root is", d._____
```

Step 9: Using the same Visual Basic workspace, under the output from your previous lab, declare and initialize myNumber and squareRoot as doubles set equal to 0.

Step 10: Write a line of code that will allow the user to enter in a value for myNumber.

Step 11: Next, add the following line of code which calls the System.Math.Sqrt( ) function:

```
squareRoot = System.Math.Sqrt(myNumber)
```

Also note the many other Math functions available for use.

Step 12: Add a line of code that will display the value of squareRoot.

Step 13: Run your program so that it works properly, and then copy and paste your code into a Word document.

Your output might look as follows:

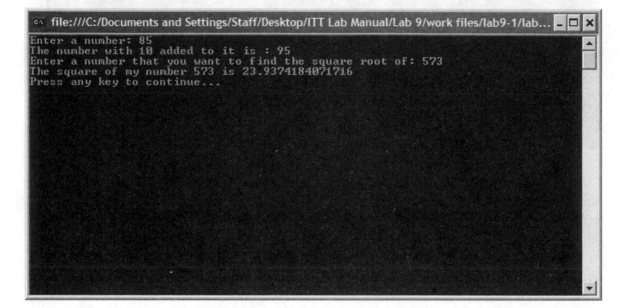

Lab 9.2 – Programming Challenge: Functions and Visual Basic

Critical Review

There are hundreds of system functions built into Visual Basic. This lab uses a random number generator, and a sleep function.

The Random Function
Visual Basic has a random number generator as a system function, called Rnd( ). The general syntax of the Rnd( ) function is as:

```
randomNum = Int(Rnd() * 20 + 1)
```

This will generate a random number between 1 and 20.

The Sleep Function
Many programming languages allow for the use of a Sleep function. This causes a delay before the next piece of code executes. The general syntax of Sleep( ) is as:

```
System.Threading.Thread.Sleep(1000)
```

This will cause a delay of 1000 milliseconds and can be changed to whatever amount of time is needed. There are 60000 milliseconds in a minute.

Demo Video: View *lab9-2.wmv* in the Lab 9 folder on the accompanying Lab Demo Media and Startup Files CD

Write the Visual Basic code for the following programming problem based on the pseudocode below.

```
The network server is going down frequently.  Write a program
that runs on the server to periodically ping the system using the
loopback address, until the issue can be resolved.  Your program
should use a random number generator to generate numbers between
1-20, in a loop that runs 200 times.  Every 1000 milliseconds,
another number should be generated.  If the random number
generator produces the number 5, then the server will be pinged.
Keep track of the number of times the server is pinged and
display the count at the end of the program.  This is the best
temporary solution to check if the server is up.
```

You must use a user defined value written function, and the system functions Rnd( ) and Sleep( ). You may use the following pseudocode to write this program in Visual Basic.

Module main()
        Declare Integer pingCounter = 0 //keeps track of the number of times server is pinged
        Call pingCounter= generateRandom(pingCounter) // this function will return pingCounter
        Display how many times the server was pinged.
End Main

```
Function generateRandom(Integer pingCounter)
        Declare Integer randonNum = 0
        Write a for loop that runs 200 iterations
                Call Rnd that generates a random number between 1 and 20 and assigns it to
randomNum such as randomNum = Int(Rnd() * 20 + 1)
                Display the random number to the screen
                If the randomNum == 5 then
                        Call pingMe()
                        Set pingCounter = pingCounter + 1
                End if
                Call Sleep(1000) such as System.Threading.Thread.Sleep(1000)
        End For
        Return pingCounter
End Function

Sub pingMe()
     Shell("Ping.exe 127.0.0.1", , True)
     Console.Out.WriteLine(" ")
End Sub
```

Your output may look as follows at the end of the run (which may take some time):

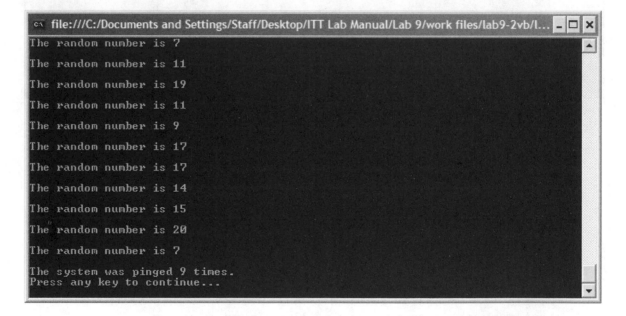

Copy and paste your Visual Basic code into a Word document.

Lab 9.3 – Input Validation

The goal of this lab is to write input validation pseudocode.

Step 1: Examine the following main module. Notice that if the user enters a capital 'Y' the program will end since the while loop only checks for a lower case 'y'.

```
Module main ()

        //Step 1: Declare variables below
        Declare String keepGoing = 'y'

        //Step 3: Loop to run program again
        While keepGoing == 'y'
                Declare Integer totalBottles = 0
                Declare Integer counter = 1
                Declare Integer todayBottles = 0
                Declare Real totalPayout = 0

                //Step 2: Call functions
                getBottles(totalBottles, todayBottles, counter)
```

```
                    calcPayout(totalBottles, totalPayout)
                    printInfo(totalBottles, totalPayout)

                    Display "Do you want to run the program again?
                    (Enter y for yes or n for no)."
                    Input keepGoing
            End While
        End Module
```

Step 2: Write a line of code that will convert the input value to a lower case value. (See Validating String Input, Page 264).

_____

_____

Step 3: Examine the getBottles module from the same program. Notice the potential input error of the user entering a negative value into todayBottles. Rewrite the module with an input validation loop inside the existing while loop that will verify that the entry into todayBottles is greater than 0. If they enter a 0 or negative value, display an error message. (Reference: Input Validation Loop, Page 258).

Previous Code

```
    //getBottles module
    Module getBottles(Integer totalBottles, Integer
    todayBottles, Integer counter)
        While counter <=7
                Display "Enter number of bottles returned for the
                day:"
                Input todayBottles
                totalBottles = totalBottles + todayBottles
                counter = counter + 1
        End While
    End Module
```

Validation Code

```
    //getBottles module
    Module getBottles(Integer totalBottles, Integer
    todayBottles, Integer counter)
        While counter <=7
```

_____

_____

_____

_____

```
                Display "Enter number of bottles returned
                for the day:"
                Input todayBottles
```

_____

_____

```
        totalBottles = totalBottles + todayBottles
        counter = counter + 1
    End While
```

```
End Module
```

Step 4: Examine the following pseudocode. Rewrite the module with a validation loop so that no less than 2 students and no more than 30 students take the test.

Previous Code

```
Module getNumber(Integer Ref number)
    Display "How many students took the test: "
    Input number
End Module
```

Validated Code

```
Module getNumber(Integer Ref number)
```

_____
_____
_____
_____
_____
_____

```
End Module
```

Step 5: Examine the following pseudocode. Rewrite the module with a validation loop so that the test score must be between 0 and 100.

Previous Code

```
Module getScores(Real Ref totalScores, Integer number, Real
score, Integer counter)
    For counter = 1 to number
        Display "Enter their score:"
        Input score
        Set totalScores = totalScores + score
    End For
End Module
```

Validated Code

```
Module getScores(Real Ref totalScores, Integer number, Real
score, Integer counter)
```

_____
_____
_____
_____
_____
_____

```
End Module
```

Lab 9.4 – Programming Challenge: Cell Phone Minute Calculator

Design and write a program that calculates and displays the number of minutes over the monthly contract minutes that a cell phone user incurred. The program should ask the user how many minutes were used during the month and how many minutes they were allowed. Validate the input as follows:

The minimum minutes allowed should be at least 200, but not greater than 800. Validate input so that the minutes allowed are between 200 and 800.
The minutes used must be over 0. Validate input so that the user does not enter a negative value.

Once correct data is entered, the program should calculate the number of minutes over the minute allowed. If minutes were not over, print a message that they were not over the limit. If minutes were over, for every minute over, a .20 fee should be added to the monthly contract rate of 74.99. Be sure not to add the .20 fee for minutes 1 to the number of minutes allowed, but rather just minutes over. Display the number of minutes used, minutes allowed, the number of minutes over, and the total due that month.

Demo Video: View *lab9-4.wmv* in the Lab 9 folder on the accompanying Lab Demo Media and Startup Files CD

You might consider the following functions:
- A function that allows the user to enter in minutes allowed within the range of 200 and 800.
- A function that allows the user to enter in the minutes used greater than or equal to 0.
- A function that calculates the total due and the total minutes over.
- A module that prints a monthly use report.

Your sample output might look as follows (note the validation code):

You may also use this pseudocode to help solve this program in Visual Basic.

```
Module main()
        //Declare local variables
        Declare String keepGoing = "y"

        While (keepGoing == "y" or keepGoing == "Y")
                Declare Integer minutesAllowed = 0
                Declare Integer minutesUsed = 0
                Declare Real totalDue = 0
                Declare Integer minutesOver = 0

                //calls functions
                Set minutesAllowed = getAllowed(minutesAllowed)
                Set minutesUsed = getUsed(minutesUsed)
                set minutesOver = calcOver(minutesAllowed, minutesUsed, minutesOver)
                Set totalDue = calcTotal(minutesAllowed, minutesUsed, totalDue, minutesOver)
                Call printData(minutesAllowed, minutesUsed, totalDue, minutesOver)
                Display "Do you want to end program? yes or no"
                Input  endProgram
        End While
End Module

Function Integer getAllowed(Integer minutesAllowed)
        Display "How many minutes are allowed"
        Input minutesAllowed
        While minutesAllowed < 200 OR minutesAllowed > 800
                Display "Please enter minutes between 200 and 800"
                Display "How many minutes are allowed"
                Input minutesAllowed
        End While
        Return minutesAllowed
End Function

Function Integer getUsed(Integer minutesUsed)
        Display "How many minutes were used"
        Input minutesUsed
        While minutesUsed < 0
                Display "Please enter minutes of at least 0"
                Display "How many minutes were used"
                Input minutesUsed
        End While
        Return minutesUsed
End Function

Function Real calcOver(Integer minutesAllowed, Integer minutesUsed, Integer minutesOver)
        If minutesUsed <= minutesAllowed then
                Set minutesOver = 0
                Display "You were not over your minutes for the month"
        Else
                Set minutesOver = minutesUsed – minutesAllowed
                Display "You were over your minutes by", minutesOver
```

```
        End If
        Return minutesOver
End Function


Function Real  calcTotal(Integer minutesAllowed, Integer minutesUsed, Real totalDue, Integer
minutesOver)
        Real extra = 0
        If minutesUsed <= minutesAllowed then
                Set totalDue = 74.99

        Else

                Set minutesOver = minutesUsed – minutesAllowed
                Set extra = minutesOver * .20
                Set totalDue = 74.99 + extra
        End If
        Return totalDue
End Function

Module printData (Integer minutesAllowed, Integer minutesUsed, Real totalDue, Integer
minutesOver)
        Display "----------------MONTHLY USE REPORT----------------------"
        Display "Minutes allowed were", minutesAllowed
        Display "Minutes used were", minutesUsed
        Display "Minutes over were", minutesOver
        Display "Total due is $", totalDue
End Module
```

Copy and paste your Visual Basic code into a Word document.

Lab 10: File Access
This lab accompanies Chapter 10 of *Starting Out with Programming Logic & Design*.

Name: _____

Lab 10.1 – File Access and Visual Basic

Critical Review

When a program needs to save data for later use, it writes the data in a file. The data can be read from the file at a later time.

Three things must happen in order to work with a file.
1) Open a file.
2) Process the file.
3) Close the file.

An internal file must be created for an output file or input file, such as:

```
Declare OutputFile myFile   //to write out
Declare InputFile myFile    //to read in
```

A data file must also be created to store the output, such as:

```
Open myFile "thedata.txt"
```

New keywords and syntax include the following:

```
Open [InternalName] [FileName]
Write [InternalName] [String or Data]
Read [InternalName] [Data]
Close [InternalName]
AppendMode  //used with Open when need to append
```

Loops are used to process the data in a file. For example:

```
For counter = 1 to 5
    Display "Enter a number:"
    Input number
    Write myFile number
End For
```

When reading information from a file and it is unknown how many items there are, use the eof function. For example:
```
While NOT eof(myFile)
    Read myFile number
    Display number
End While
```

In Visual Basic, you create a text file to write out to it such as:

```
Dim writer As System.IO.StreamWriter =
System.IO.File.CreateText("myRecords.txt")
```

In Visual Basic, you pull data in from a file such as:

```
Dim reader As System.IO.StreamReader =
System.IO.File.OpenText("myRecords.txt")
```

Help Video: Double click the file to view video

lab10-1.wmv

This lab examines how to work with a file by writing Visual Basic code. Read the following programming problem prior to completing the lab.

```
Write and design a simple program that will take 3 pieces
of data and write it to a file.  Create variables and set
them equal to the appropriate values:

Declare string firstName = "xxx"
Declare string lastName = "xxx"
Declare integer age = your age

Write this information to a file called myRecords.txt.
Next, read this information from the file and print it to
the screen.
```

Step 1: Create a new Visual Basic workspace and add the following code:

```
Module Module1

    Sub Main()

        Dim firstName As String = "XXXX"
        Dim lastName As String = "XXX"
        Dim age As Integer = ####

        Dim writer As System.IO.StreamWriter =
System.IO.File.CreateText("myRecords.txt")
        writer.WriteLine(firstName & " " & lastName & " " & age)
        writer.Close()

        Dim reader As System.IO.StreamReader =
System.IO.File.OpenText("myRecords.txt")
        Dim myInfo As String = reader.ReadLine()
        Console.WriteLine(myInfo)
        reader.Close()
```

```
        'this causes a pause so you can see your program
        Console.Write("Press enter to continue...")
        Console.ReadLine()
    End Sub

End Module
```

Step 2: Change the values of the variables to your records.

Step 3: Run the program so that it works, and view your .txt file.

PASTE VISUAL BASIC CODE HERE

PASTE TEXT FILE CONTENTS HERE

Lab 10.2 – File Access and Nested Loops

The purpose of this lab is to make lab 10.1 more efficient by adding nested loops, variables to store the data, and read the data in to the file and from the file more efficient.

Help Video: Double click the file to view video

lab10-2.wmv

Step 1: Create a new Visual Basic workspace and save to the proper location.

Step 2: Inside main, declare a string variable named runAgain and initialize it to "yes".

Step 3: Next, create a while loop that will run as long as runAgain = "yes".   The following steps should all be placed inside this outer loop. This outside loop should look like:

```
Dim runAgain As String = "yes"
While runAgain = "yes"
    'all other code will go in here


    Console.Write("Do you want to run again yes or no: ")
    runAgain = Console.ReadLine()
    'this causes a pause so you can see your program
    Console.Write("Press enter to continue...")
    Console.ReadLine()
End While
```

Step 4: Inside the loop you just coded, create the following variables:

```
Dim firstName As String = " "
Dim lastName As String = " "
Dim age As Integer = 0
Dim anotherInput As String = "yes"
Dim howMany As Integer = 0
```

Step 5: Next, create an inner while loop that will run as long as anotherInput = "yes". This loop will be used to input data into the text file and should look as follows:

```
While anotherInput = "yes"
    'code for inputing data into file goes in this loop

    Console.Write("Is there another input yes or no: ")
    anotherInput = Console.ReadLine()
End While
```

Step 6: Next, inside that loop, create a writer variable using streamWriter such as:

```
        Dim writer As System.IO.StreamWriter =
        System.IO.File.AppendText("myRecords.txt")
```

Step 7: Next, add the following lines that will enter values into the variables.

```
        Console.Write("Enter the first name: ")
        firstName = Console.ReadLine()
        Console.Write("Enter the last name: ")
        lastName = Console.ReadLine()
        Console.Write("Enter the age: ")
        age = Console.ReadLine()
```

Step 8: Next, write the data from the variables to the file, close the writer variable, and increment how many. This code should look as follows:

```
        writer.WriteLine(firstName & " " & lastName & " " & age)
        writer.Close()
        howMany = howMany + 1
```

Step 9: That ends the input for writing information to the file. Outside of the loop that inputs another person, declare a lineInput variable and a reader variable that will allow us to read the data in from a file. This code should look as follows:

```
        Dim lineInput As String
        Dim reader As IO.StreamReader
        reader = IO.File.OpenText("myrecords.txt")
```

Step 10: Finally, add a Do Until loop that will use the Peek( ) function to read data into your program and print it to the screen. Outside of that loop, close the reader file. This code should look as follows:

```
        Do Until reader.Peek() = -1
            lineInput = reader.ReadLine()
            Console.WriteLine(lineInput)
        Loop
        reader.Close()
```

Step 11: Based on what you just coded, answer the following questions:
   a. What is the name of your text file? _____
   b. How did you get the data to append to a file? _____
   c. How many loops did you code in this program? _____
   d. What does the Peek( ) function do? _____

Step 12: Run the program so that it works, and view your .txt file.

PASTE VISUAL BASIC CODE HERE

PASTE TEXT FILE CONTENTS HERE